Max Lucado Magnetic Journal

Max Lucado quotes are from his books.
Used by permission of the W Publishing Group,
a division of Thomas Nelson, Inc. All rights reserved.

ISBN 1-60116-008-9

Printed in China

To abide in Christ's love is to make His love your home.

MAX LUCADO

What makes us special is the signature of God on our lives.

MAX LUCADO

Of all we don't know about the creation,
there is one thing we do know—God did it with a smile.

MAX LUCADO

We exist to exhibit God, to display His glory.

MAX LUCADO

Probe deep within God. Explore every corner.
Search every angle. Love is all you find.

MAX LUCADO

With God, every day matters, every person counts.

MAX LUCADO

We live in an art gallery of divine creativity.

MAX LUCADO

It is when we are out of options that we are most ready for God's surprises.

MAX LUCADO

Let God be God. Let Him bathe you in His glory.
Take a moment to be still, and know that He is God.

MAX LUCADO

God's love supply is never empty.

MAX LUCADO

We can drink deeply and often of His unfailing love.

MAX LUCADO

As a tree draws nutrients from the soil,
we draw nourishment from the Father.

MAX LUCADO

Look up reliability in heaven's dictionary and read
its one word definition: God.

MAX LUCADO

Yes, God is in heaven. Yes, He rules the universe.
He's still near enough to touch. Strong enough to trust.

MAX LUCADO

May our lives be impassioned only by faith...
be influenced only by God...be taught only by Christ.

MAX LUCADO

We are God's idea. We are His. His face. His eyes. His hands. His touch...
There is no greater truth than this: We are His. Unalterably.
He loves us. Undyingly.

MAX LUCADO

To abide in Christ's love is to make His love your home.

MAX LUCADO

What makes us special is the signature of God on our lives.

MAX LUCADO

Of all we don't know about the creation,
there is one thing we do know—God did it with a smile.

MAX LUCADO

We exist to exhibit God, to display His glory.

MAX LUCADO

Probe deep within God. Explore every corner.
Search every angle. Love is all you find.

MAX LUCADO

With God, every day matters, every person counts.

MAX LUCADO

We live in an art gallery of divine creativity.

MAX LUCADO

It is when we are out of options that we are most ready for God's surprises.

MAX LUCADO

Let God be God. Let Him bathe you in His glory.
Take a moment to be still, and know that He is God.

MAX LUCADO

God's love supply is never empty.
MAX LUCADO

We can drink deeply and often of His unfailing love.

MAX LUCADO

As a tree draws nutrients from the soil,
we draw nourishment from the Father.

MAX LUCADO

Look up reliability in heaven's dictionary and read
its one word definition: God.

MAX LUCADO

Yes, God is in heaven. Yes, He rules the universe.
He's still near enough to touch. Strong enough to trust.

MAX LUCADO

May our lives be impassioned only by faith...
be influenced only by God...be taught only by Christ.

MAX LUCADO

We are God's idea. We are His. His face. His eyes. His hands. His touch...
There is no greater truth than this: We are His. Unalterably.
He loves us. Undyingly.

MAX LUCADO

To abide in Christ's love is to make His love your home.

MAX LUCADO

What makes us special is the signature of God on our lives.

MAX LUCADO

Of all we don't know about the creation,
there is one thing we do know—God did it with a smile.

MAX LUCADO

We exist to exhibit God, to display His glory.

MAX LUCADO

Probe deep within God. Explore every corner.
Search every angle. Love is all you find.

MAX LUCADO

With God, every day matters, every person counts.

MAX LUCADO

We live in an art gallery of divine creativity.

MAX LUCADO

It is when we are out of options that we are most ready for God's surprises.

MAX LUCADO

Let God be God. Let Him bathe you in His glory.
Take a moment to be still, and know that He is God.

MAX LUCADO

God's love supply is never empty.

MAX LUCADO

We can drink deeply and often of His unfailing love.

MAX LUCADO

As a tree draws nutrients from the soil,
we draw nourishment from the Father.

MAX LUCADO

Look up reliability in heaven's dictionary and read
its one word definition: God.

MAX LUCADO

Yes, God is in heaven. Yes, He rules the universe.
He's still near enough to touch. Strong enough to trust.

MAX LUCADO

May our lives be impassioned only by faith...
be influenced only by God...be taught only by Christ.

MAX LUCADO

We are God's idea. We are His. His face. His eyes. His hands. His touch...
There is no greater truth than this: We are His. Unalterably.
He loves us. Undyingly.

MAX LUCADO

To abide in Christ's love is to make His love your home.

MAX LUCADO

What makes us special is the signature of God on our lives.

MAX LUCADO

Of all we don't know about the creation,
there is one thing we do know—God did it with a smile.

MAX LUCADO

We exist to exhibit God, to display His glory.

MAX LUCADO

Probe deep within God. Explore every corner.
Search every angle. Love is all you find.

MAX LUCADO

With God, every day matters, every person counts.

MAX LUCADO

We live in an art gallery of divine creativity.

MAX LUCADO

It is when we are out of options that we are most ready for God's surprises.

MAX LUCADO

Let God be God. Let Him bathe you in His glory.
Take a moment to be still, and know that He is God.

MAX LUCADO

God's love supply is never empty.

MAX LUCADO

We can drink deeply and often of His unfailing love.

MAX LUCADO

As a tree draws nutrients from the soil,
we draw nourishment from the Father.

MAX LUCADO

Look up reliability in heaven's dictionary and read
its one word definition: God.

MAX LUCADO

Yes, God is in heaven. Yes, He rules the universe.
He's still near enough to touch. Strong enough to trust.

MAX LUCADO

May our lives be impassioned only by faith...
be influenced only by God...be taught only by Christ.

MAX LUCADO

We are God's idea. We are His. His face. His eyes. His hands. His touch…
There is no greater truth than this: We are His. Unalterably.
He loves us. Undyingly.

MAX LUCADO

To abide in Christ's love is to make His love your home.

MAX LUCADO

What makes us special is the signature of God on our lives.

MAX LUCADO

Of all we don't know about the creation,
there is one thing we do know—God did it with a smile.

MAX LUCADO

We exist to exhibit God, to display His glory.

MAX LUCADO

Probe deep within God. Explore every corner.
Search every angle. Love is all you find.

MAX LUCADO

With God, every day matters, every person counts.
MAX LUCADO

We live in an art gallery of divine creativity.

MAX LUCADO

It is when we are out of options that we are most ready for God's surprises.

MAX LUCADO

Let God be God. Let Him bathe you in His glory.
Take a moment to be still, and know that He is God.

MAX LUCADO

God's love supply is never empty.

MAX LUCADO

We can drink deeply and often of His unfailing love.

MAX LUCADO

As a tree draws nutrients from the soil,
we draw nourishment from the Father.

MAX LUCADO

Look up reliability in heaven's dictionary and read
its one word definition: God.

MAX LUCADO

Yes, God is in heaven. Yes, He rules the universe.
He's still near enough to touch. Strong enough to trust.

MAX LUCADO

May our lives be impassioned only by faith...
be influenced only by God...be taught only by Christ.

MAX LUCADO

We are God's idea. We are His. His face. His eyes. His hands. His touch...
There is no greater truth than this: We are His. Unalterably.
He loves us. Undyingly.

MAX LUCADO

To abide in Christ's love is to make His love your home.

MAX LUCADO

What makes us special is the signature of God on our lives.

MAX LUCADO

Of all we don't know about the creation,
there is one thing we do know—God did it with a smile.

MAX LUCADO

We exist to exhibit God, to display His glory.

MAX LUCADO

Probe deep within God. Explore every corner.
Search every angle. Love is all you find.

MAX LUCADO

With God, every day matters, every person counts.

MAX LUCADO

We live in an art gallery of divine creativity.

MAX LUCADO

It is when we are out of options that we are most ready for God's surprises.

MAX LUCADO

Let God be God. Let Him bathe you in His glory.
Take a moment to be still, and know that He is God.

MAX LUCADO

God's love supply is never empty.

MAX LUCADO

We can drink deeply and often of His unfailing love.

MAX LUCADO

As a tree draws nutrients from the soil,
we draw nourishment from the Father.

MAX LUCADO

Look up reliability in heaven's dictionary and read
its one word definition: God.

MAX LUCADO

Yes, God is in heaven. Yes, He rules the universe.
He's still near enough to touch. Strong enough to trust.

MAX LUCADO

May our lives be impassioned only by faith...
be influenced only by God...be taught only by Christ.

MAX LUCADO

We are God's idea. We are His. His face. His eyes. His hands. His touch...
There is no greater truth than this: We are His. Unalterably.
He loves us. Undyingly.

MAX LUCADO

To abide in Christ's love is to make His love your home.

MAX LUCADO

What makes us special is the signature of God on our lives.

MAX LUCADO

Of all we don't know about the creation,
there is one thing we do know—God did it with a smile.

MAX LUCADO

We exist to exhibit God, to display His glory.

MAX LUCADO

Probe deep within God. Explore every corner.
Search every angle. Love is all you find.

MAX LUCADO

With God, every day matters, every person counts.

MAX LUCADO

We live in an art gallery of divine creativity.

MAX LUCADO

It is when we are out of options that we are most ready for God's surprises.

MAX LUCADO

Let God be God. Let Him bathe you in His glory.
Take a moment to be still, and know that He is God.

MAX LUCADO

God's love supply is never empty.

MAX LUCADO

We can drink deeply and often of His unfailing love.

MAX LUCADO

As a tree draws nutrients from the soil,
we draw nourishment from the Father.

MAX LUCADO

Look up reliability in heaven's dictionary and read
its one word definition: God.

MAX LUCADO

Yes, God is in heaven. Yes, He rules the universe.
He's still near enough to touch. Strong enough to trust.

MAX LUCADO

May our lives be impassioned only by faith…
be influenced only by God…be taught only by Christ.

MAX LUCADO

We are God's idea. We are His. His face. His eyes. His hands. His touch...
There is no greater truth than this: We are His. Unalterably.
He loves us. Undyingly.

MAX LUCADO

To abide in Christ's love is to make His love your home.

MAX LUCADO

What makes us special is the signature of God on our lives.

MAX LUCADO

Of all we don't know about the creation,
there is one thing we do know—God did it with a smile.

MAX LUCADO

We exist to exhibit God, to display His glory.

MAX LUCADO

Probe deep within God. Explore every corner.
Search every angle. Love is all you find.

MAX LUCADO

With God, every day matters, every person counts.
MAX LUCADO

We live in an art gallery of divine creativity.

MAX LUCADO

It is when we are out of options that we are most ready for God's surprises.

MAX LUCADO

Let God be God. Let Him bathe you in His glory.
Take a moment to be still, and know that He is God.

MAX LUCADO

God's love supply is never empty.

MAX LUCADO

We can drink deeply and often of His unfailing love.

MAX LUCADO

As a tree draws nutrients from the soil,
we draw nourishment from the Father.

MAX LUCADO

Look up reliability in heaven's dictionary and read
its one word definition: God.

MAX LUCADO

Yes, God is in heaven. Yes, He rules the universe.
He's still near enough to touch. Strong enough to trust.

MAX LUCADO

May our lives be impassioned only by faith...
be influenced only by God...be taught only by Christ.

MAX LUCADO

We are God's idea. We are His. His face. His eyes. His hands. His touch...
There is no greater truth than this: We are His. Unalterably.
He loves us. Undyingly.

MAX LUCADO

To abide in Christ's love is to make His love your home.

MAX LUCADO

What makes us special is the signature of God on our lives.

MAX LUCADO

Of all we don't know about the creation,
there is one thing we do know—God did it with a smile.

MAX LUCADO

We exist to exhibit God, to display His glory.

MAX LUCADO

Probe deep within God. Explore every corner.
Search every angle. Love is all you find.

MAX LUCADO

With God, every day matters, every person counts.

MAX LUCADO

We live in an art gallery of divine creativity.

MAX LUCADO

It is when we are out of options that we are most ready for God's surprises.

MAX LUCADO

Let God be God. Let Him bathe you in His glory.
Take a moment to be still, and know that He is God.

MAX LUCADO

God's love supply is never empty.

MAX LUCADO

We can drink deeply and often of His unfailing love.

MAX LUCADO

As a tree draws nutrients from the soil,
we draw nourishment from the Father.

MAX LUCADO

Look up reliability in heaven's dictionary and read
its one word definition: God.

MAX LUCADO

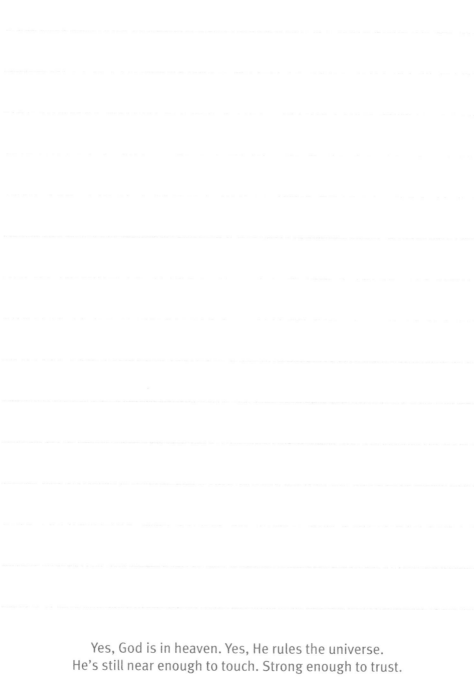

Yes, God is in heaven. Yes, He rules the universe.
He's still near enough to touch. Strong enough to trust.

MAX LUCADO

May our lives be impassioned only by faith...
be influenced only by God...be taught only by Christ.

MAX LUCADO

We are God's idea. We are His. His face. His eyes. His hands. His touch...
There is no greater truth than this: We are His. Unalterably.
He loves us. Undyingly.

MAX LUCADO

To abide in Christ's love is to make His love your home.
MAX LUCADO

What makes us special is the signature of God on our lives.

MAX LUCADO

Of all we don't know about the creation,
there is one thing we do know—God did it with a smile.

MAX LUCADO

We exist to exhibit God, to display His glory.

MAX LUCADO

Probe deep within God. Explore every corner.
Search every angle. Love is all you find.

MAX LUCADO

With God, every day matters, every person counts.
MAX LUCADO